The Funky B Fiddle book

the complete workbook for learning to play

by K. J. Liley

with artwork by children from Arbroath and Carnoustie

This book belongs to_____

School_____Class_____

My fiddle's name is_____

The Funky Beginners Fiddle Book

First paperback edition printed 2016 in the United Kingdom.
A catalogue record for this book is available from the British Library.
ISBN 978-1-911270-08-9

Published by Lovaig Music.
Designed and Set by K. J. Liley, Lovaig Music.

Acknowledgement
Thank you to Davey, Katy, Heather Miranda, Danie Hutchin, Elaine Hunter, Peter Hunter, Caroline Masson, Lauren Hall-Lew, Scott Burrell, Pamela Grant and all my family, friends, colleagues and pupils.

Lovaig.Music@gmail.com
www.LovaigMusic.com

ISBN 978-1-911270-08-9

9 781911 270089 >

Introduction ★

Hello and welcome to the book!
Collect stars by colouring them in when you complete each activity.
How many can you collect in each chapter?
Can your friends match your high score?
Look out for the friendly monsters and aliens who have tips to help you play. Try your best to play every day - and have fun!

Did you know that fiddles and violins are exactly the same thing?
There's no difference at all!

Contents

Questions

Scales, Arpeggios & Mini Tunes

Tunes

Chapter One

What are the parts of my instrument?

1. Scroll	2. Fingerboard	3. Neck	4. Chin Rest
5. Pegs	6. Bridge	7. Tail Piece	8. Fine Tuners
9. E String	10. A String	11. D String	12. G String
13. F holes	14. C Bout	15. Shoulder Rest	

☆ 1. Write in all the part names with a pencil!   *Puzzle*

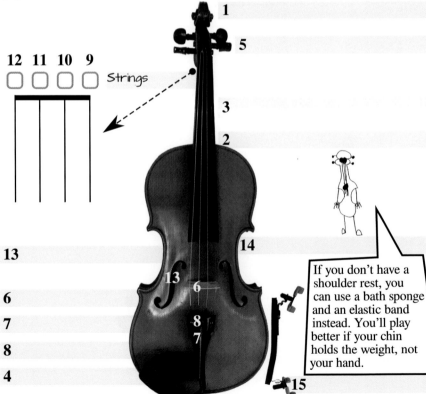

12 11 10 9
◯ ◯ ◯ ◯ Strings

13
6
7
8
4

If you don't have a shoulder rest, you can use a bath sponge and an elastic band instead. You'll play better if your chin holds the weight, not your hand.

What can we play first?

1. Hold your instrument in *banjo position*, on your knee and flat against your middle.
2. The *scroll* goes to your left.
3. Plucking the strings with your right thumb, explore the sounds and then try your first tunes.
4. Use the string names you found on page 1 for these tunes.

 2. Sailing *Tune*

AAAA AAAA DDEE ADAE
AAAA AAAA DDEE ADA

 3. Twinkles *Tune*

DDDD GGDD GGDD AADD
DDGG DDAA DDGG DDAA
DDDD GGDD GGDD AADD

 4. Now try making up your own tune. *Puzzle*

My tune is called... _____

_____

_____

2

What are the names of the notes?

If you look carefully, you can see that the round part of each note is either on a line or in a space between the lines. The notes on the lines say...

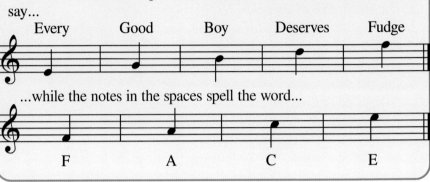

Every   Good   Boy   Deserves   Fudge

...while the notes in the spaces spell the word...

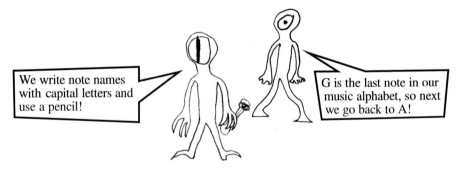

F   A   C   E

We write note names with capital letters and use a pencil!

G is the last note in our music alphabet, so next we go back to A!

 5. Write *line* or *space* and the name of each note. The first one is done for you!   *Puzzle*

Line, E

6. Here they are again, all mixed up. *Puzzle*

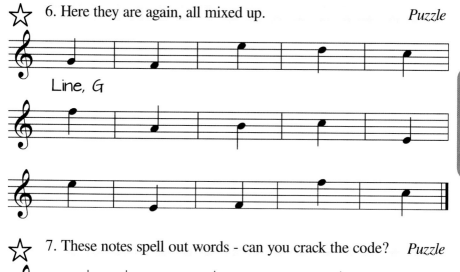

Line, G

7. These notes spell out words - can you crack the code? *Puzzle*

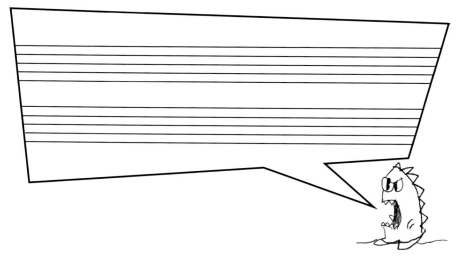

B   A   A

8. Write your own secret message here. Can your friends read it?

How long does each note last?

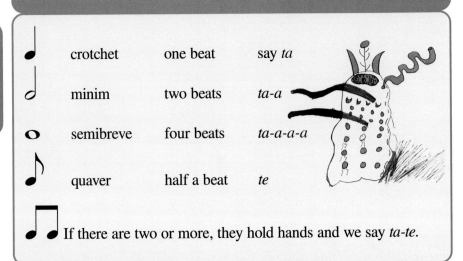

♩	crotchet	one beat	say *ta*
♩	minim	two beats	*ta-a*
o	semibreve	four beats	*ta-a-a-a*
♪	quaver	half a beat	*te*

If there are two or more, they hold hands and we say *ta-te*.

☆ 9. How many beats do each of these notes last for? *Puzzle*

♫ ☐   ♩ ☐   ♪ ☐   o ☐   ♩ ☐

☆ 10. Music sums! *Puzzle*

A. ♩ + ♩ = ☐

B. ♩ + ♩ = ☐

C. ♩ + ♩ = ☐

D. ♪ + ♪ = ☐

E. ♩ + ♩ + ♩ = ☐

F. ♫ + ☐ = ♩

5

Why do some stems go up and others down?

1. It's to make it look tidy - it doesn't make any other difference.
2. Notes below the middle line usually have stems going up on the right while notes above hang down on the left.
3. Notes on the middle line can go either way.

 11. Draw in the stems for these notes. *Puzzle*

 12. Say, then clap, each of these rhythms. *Puzzle*
       Use a metronome (app or website) to help you.

A.

B.

C.

D.

E.

F.

6

On your left hand you have a number on each finger...

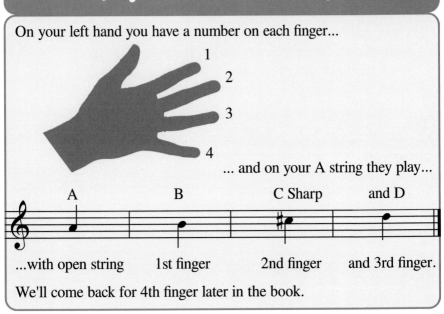

1
2
3
4

... and on your A string they play...

A   B   C Sharp   and D

...with open string   1st finger   2nd finger   and 3rd finger.

We'll come back for 4th finger later in the book.

13. How many fingers on the A string do you need for each note?

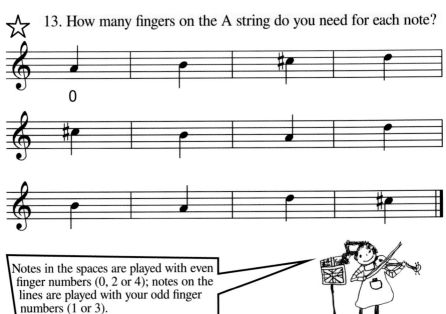

0

Notes in the spaces are played with even finger numbers (0, 2 or 4); notes on the lines are played with your odd finger numbers (1 or 3).

7

Where do my fingers go on A?

1. Start with your instrument in banjo position, plucking gently with your right thumb.
2. This makes it easy to see what you're doing.
3. Keep space for a marble behind your first finger and before your second.

G D A E

B
C#
D

☆ 14. Notes on A   *Exercise*

The letters you see under the notes are not the note names, they are chord symbols. They let other instruments join in with us.

☆ 15. Hot Cross Buns   *Song*

A E A   A E A   A   B m   A E A

☆ 16. Yankee Doodle   *Song*

A   E   A   E 7

A   D   E 7   A

How do I play notes on the D string?

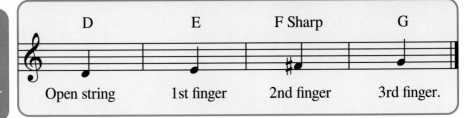

D	E	F Sharp	G
Open string	1st finger	2nd finger	3rd finger.

☆ 17. Which finger on the D string would play each of these notes?

I don't believe I can read music!

Ask yourself three questions as you go along;
1. What is the name of the note?
2. How do I play it?
3. How long does it last?
You are reading music!
It gets easier the more you do it.

Do you notice the dots at the start and end of the lines?
Those are repeat marks so we play that part again.

9

Where do my fingers go on D?

1. Your fingers go in the same places as they did on A.
2. Don't forget space for a marble between 1st and 2nd fingers!
3. You also want space for an orange between your wrist and your instrument.

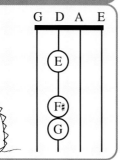

18. Notes on D   *Exercise*

19. Au Clair De La Lune (By The Light Of The Moon)   *Lullaby*

20. Pije Kuba do Jakuba (Jake Drinks To Jacob)   *Polish Song*

21. Mary Had A Little Lamb   *Song*

How do I get my instrument onto my shoulder?

☆ 22.

> Hold your instrument in rest position - be careful where you put your left hand.

> Use two hands to lift it up...

> ...and up!

> Find a comfy spot for your instrument on your shoulder, under your chin.

> Use your finger to pluck. Your elbow is high for G and lower for each other string.

> Move your left hand down the neck until you feel the bump. Keep the space inside your wrist!

Argh! It's all too much at once!

That's okay - you can always take things one step at a time.
Play each of your tunes in banjo position first, then up on your shoulder when you're ready. If you watch yourself in the mirror, it'll help you see what you're doing.

11

23. A Magic Trick!

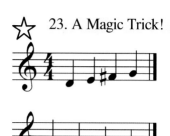

1. Play this bar in banjo position.
2. Keep your fingers on the strings while you move your instrument onto your shoulder.
3. Now play this bar with your instrument on your shoulder. Your fingers are in the right place already!

24. The Grand Old Duke of York

Singing Game

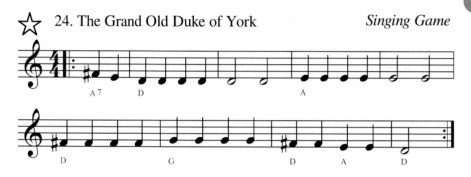

25. Pease Pudding Hot

Song

26. Spaces

Exercise

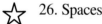

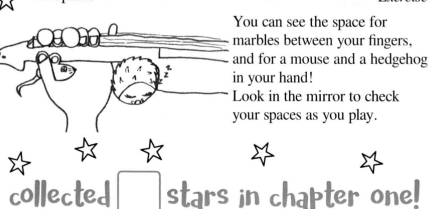

You can see the space for marbles between your fingers, and for a mouse and a hedgehog in your hand!
Look in the mirror to check your spaces as you play.

I collected ☐ stars in chapter one!

Chapter Two

What are the parts of my bow?

1. Stick   2. Hair   3. Point   4. Lapping   5. Screw
6. Frog   7. Heel   8. Rosin   9. Ferrule

2

☆ 1. Use the numbers to write in all the part names!   *Puzzle*

3

8

2

1

4

9

6

7

5

Turn the screw to tighten the bow a little before you play. Remember to loosen it again when you stop!

What is rosin?

Rosin is STICKY stuff that we rub on the bow. It smashes easily so keep your thumb over the metal part of the bow (ferrule) as you use it. Without rosin, our bow would make no sound at all!

13

How do I hold my bow?

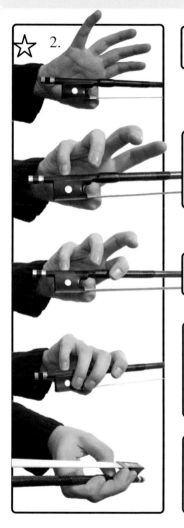

☆ 2.

Bend your right thumb and sit your bow on the end.

Bend your pinkie (little finger) and sit it on top of the stick, on its point too.
Try to balance!

Sit your index finger over the lapping (silver or stripey bit).

Now let the other two sit down in between. You want a wee space between each one. If it feels a bit wobbly that's okay!
It's a balance and not a grip!

Turn your bow over to check your bow hold. Is there a corner in your thumb?
Could you fit an egg in your hand?

This shape looks like the frog of your bow. ⊓
When you see it, start at the heel and play a down bow.
This shape looks like the other end, ⋁ so it means the opposite.
When you see these lines, ∥ draw a hoop in the air with your bow.

14

What are rests?

Each of the note lengths we met on p.13 has a rest to match.
We count the same way, but these are silent *notes you don't play.*

⁊	quaver rest	half a beat	*se*
𝄽	crotchet rest	one beat	*sa*
▬	minim rest	two beats	*sa-a*
▬	semibreve rest	four beats	*sa-a-a-a*

☆ 3. How many beats do each of these rests last for? *Puzzle*

Two of the rests look like hats!
Keep your hat on if you're not
staying long; take it off if you're
here for longer!

☆ 4. Music sums *Puzzle*

A. 𝅗𝅥 + 𝄽 = ☐

B. ▬ + 𝅘𝅥 = ☐

C. 𝅗𝅥 + ▬ = ☐

D. ⁊ + 𝅘𝅥𝅮 = ☐

E. 𝄽 + 𝅗𝅥 + 𝅘𝅥 = ☐

F. 𝅘𝅥𝅮𝅘𝅥𝅮 + ☐ = 𝅗𝅥

How do I use my bow?

☆ 5.

1. Watch yourself in the mirror.
2. Sit your bow on the string, half way between the *bridge* and the *fingerboard*.
3. Start at the end under your hand (*the heel*) and pull it all the way down to the point, keeping parallel with the bridge.
4. Draw a hula hoop in the air with your bow hand and land gently back where you started; and repeat!
5. Show your teacher the funny noises you find, and s/he will help!

☆ 6. Hula Hoops and Open Strings   *Exercise*
      Count to 4 in the down bow, and four in the hoop.

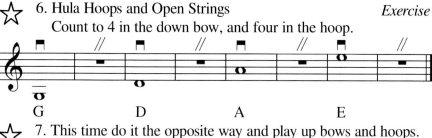

G   D   A   E

☆ 7. This time do it the opposite way and play up bows and hoops.

☆ 8. Next, count to 4 on a down bow and then 4 back up. No hoops!

☆ 9. Hula Hoops and Notes on the D String.

16

Can we use notes from D and A together?

1. Here are the notes we know, all together.
2. When we play them in order it is called a 'scale'.
3. This one starts on D, so it is called the *D Major Scale*.
4. Have you noticed that they go in alphabetical order?
5. G is the last note in the music alphabet, so next we go back to A.

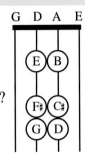

10. Name each note, and write in how to play it. Revise Chapter 1 if you're stuck!   *Puzzle*

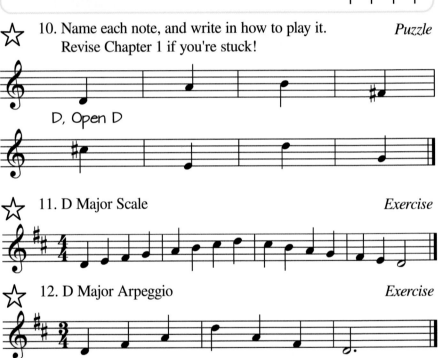

D, Open D

11. D Major Scale   *Exercise*

12. D Major Arpeggio   *Exercise*

What has happened to the sharps?

Until now, we have had a sharp symbol in front of each note where we needed it. That looks a bit messy, so now we'll tidy them up to the start of the line. We'll find out more about this later in the book!

How do I cross the strings?

1. Keep your bow elbow the same height as your bow hand.
2. They move together, higher for the D string and lower for A.
3. It looks like a window opening!

☆ 13. Twinkle Twinkle Little Star   *Song*

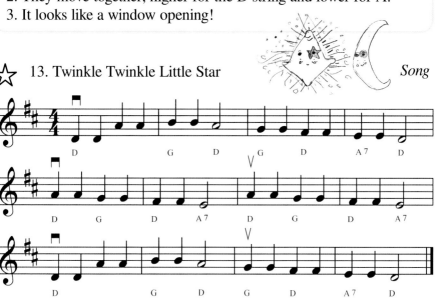

☆ 14. Donald Where's Yer Troosers?   *Song, Andy Stewart, 1960*
With the kind permission of the copyright owner, Kerr's Music Corporation.

☆ 15. Knees Up Mother Brown   *Song*

18

How do I play on the E string?

We draw *ledger lines* like steps above or below the stave when we want to play higher or lower notes. They continue the pattern we already know. The higher notes are...

E	F sharp	G sharp	and	A
0	1	2		3

2

☆ 16. Here are notes on the E string.   *Puzzle*
Write the note name and the finger number under each note.

E, 0

Where do my fingers go on E?

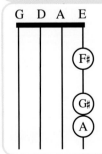

1. Your fingers go in the same places as they did on A and D.
2. Don't forget spaces for marbles!
3. You also want space for an orange between your wrist and your instrument.

17. Pease Pudding Hot — *Song*

18. A Major Scale — *Exercise*

19. A Major Arpeggio — *Exercise*

2

20. A Sailor Went To Sea — *Song*

21. Old MacDonald Had A Farm — *Song*

How do I play on G?

The ledger lines look like a ladder down to G. The notes are...

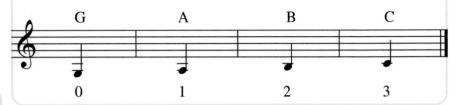

G	A	B	C
0	1	2	3

2 ☆ 22. Here are notes on the G string. *Puzzle*
Write the note name and the finger number under each note.

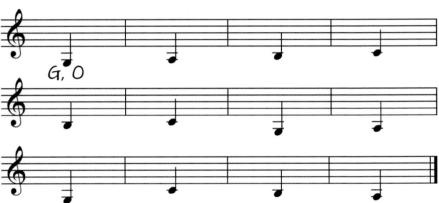

G, 0

Where do my fingers go on G?

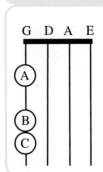

G D A E

(A)

(B)

(C)

1. Your fingers go in the same places again.
2. Don't forget space for a marble!
3. You still need that space for an orange between your wrist and your instrument.

It's normal to worry that you might be wrong. Don't let it put you off - it's okay to make mistakes!

Chapter Three

How long do notes and rests last?

Here are the note and rest lengths we have met so far, along with some new ones for Chapter 3.

How many beats?	Name	Note	Say	Rest	Say
4	Semibreve	𝅝	ta-a-a-a	▬	sa-a-a-a
3	Dotted Minim	𝅗𝅥.	ta-a-a	▬.	sa-a-a
2	Minim	𝅗𝅥	ta-a	▬	sa-a
1 + ½	Dotted Crotchet	𝅘𝅥.	taa	𝄾.	saa
1	Crotchet	𝅘𝅥	ta	𝄾	sa
¾	Dotted Quaver	𝅘𝅥𝅮.	(ta-) te	𝄿.	se
½	Quavers	𝅘𝅥𝅮 𝅘𝅥𝅮𝅘𝅥𝅮	(ta-) te	𝄿	se
¼	Semiquavers	𝅘𝅥𝅯 𝅘𝅥𝅯𝅘𝅥𝅯𝅘𝅥𝅯𝅘𝅥𝅯	ta-fa-ti-fe	𝅀	si

☆ 1. How many beats are each of these worth?   *Puzzle*
   Draw lines to match up the notes, rests, and their numbers.

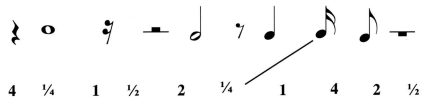

4   ¼   1   ½   2   ¼   1   4   2   ½

What are bars?

Have you noticed that each line of music is split into boxes?
We call the boxes *bars* and the lines in between them *bar lines*.
A *double bar line* says *the end*, and with two dots; *repeat*.

☆ 2. Count the beats in each bar, and write the number above the 4.

What is a time signature?

A *time signature* looks like a fraction at the start of a tune.
The *4* on the bottom says that we are counting *single beats*.
The number on top is the number of *beats* we count in the *bar*.

☆ 3. Write in a note or rest to complete each bar.   *Puzzle*

☆ 4. What do we call the lines that split the music into boxes?

Say 'ssh!' in the rests!
Your metronome will help you to keep a steady beat.

24

What are dots for?

1. There are two beats in this bar.

2. If you draw an arm on one of the notes, we chop it in half. The other half has to go somewhere...

3. ...here it is. Can you see the dot?

4. The first note now lasts for 1 + ½ beats, and the second note now lasts only ½ a beat, so; *a dot makes the note last half as long again.*

☆ 5. Music sums

Puzzle

A. 𝅘𝅥 + 𝅘𝅥 = ☐

B. 𝅘𝅥. + 𝅘𝅥𝅮 = ☐

C. 𝅘𝅥𝅮 + 𝅘𝅥. = ☐

D. 𝅗𝅥 + 𝅗𝅥 = ☐

E. 𝅗𝅥 + 𝅘𝅥 = ☐

F. 𝅗𝅥. + 𝅘𝅥 = ☐

G. 𝅘𝅥𝅮 + 𝅘𝅥𝅮 = ☐

H. 𝅘𝅥𝅮 + 𝅘𝅥𝅮. = ☐

I. 𝅝 + 𝅝 = ☐

J. 𝅝. + 𝅗𝅥 = ☐

6. Draw dots to make these bars add up. *Puzzle*

The treble clef is a big letter G and is like a target showing you where G is. *Clef* is french for *key* - it's your key to all the other notes.

7. Trace over the treble clef and then draw more of your own. Start in the middle of the spiral!

8. London Bridge Is Falling Down *Song*

9. Two Football Songs *Chants*

3

26

What are dynamics?

1. *Dynamics* are our volume control when we play music.
2. They give our tunes shape and expression.
3. This table shows you the symbols.
4. In some styles of music the dynamics are already on the page.
5. Otherwise we write in our own.

	crescendo	gradually louder
ƒƒƒ	*fortississimo*	loudest
ƒƒ	*fortissimo*	louder
ƒ	*forte*	loud
mƒ	*mezzo forte*	moderately loud
mp	*mezzo piano*	moderately quiet
p	*piano*	quiet
pp	*pianissimo*	quieter
ppp	*pianississimo*	quietest
	diminuendo	gradually quieter

☆ 10. Using Dynamics   *Puzzle*

Pick your favourite tune and split it into phrases by drawing commas. Use symbols from the table to show how loud or quiet you want to play each phrase.
Use a pencil so you can try it in different ways.

☆ 11. The Can-Can   *Jacques Offenbach, 1858*
Write in your dynamics under the tune!

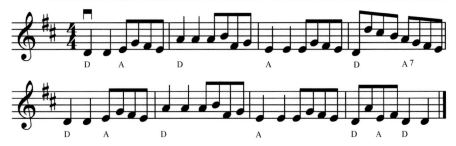

What is a key?

1. Every tune is made from a scale - the *key* tells you which one.
2. If you know what *key* a tune is in, you know which notes to play.
3. You can tell what *key* a tune is in by looking at the *key signature*; count the sharps and say to yourself...

Go   Down   And   Enter   By   Fours

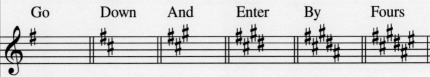

1 sharp says G, 2 sharps say D...watch out, 6 sharps say F *sharp*!

☆ 15. What key?   *Puzzle*

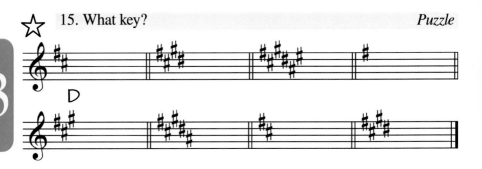

D

☆ 16. What scale would you practise before playing each of these?

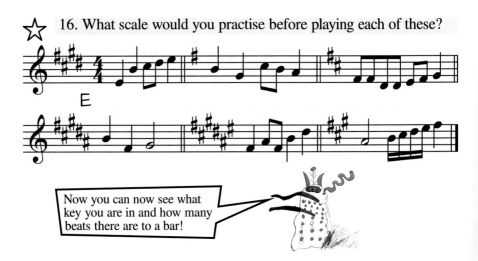

E

Now you can now see what key you are in and how many beats there are to a bar!

17. Nah Nah! — *Taunt*

18. See-Saw — *Playground Song*

19. Mo Chùrachan (The Fairy Lullaby) — *Gaelic Lullaby*

3

Help, I keep running out of bow!

Move the bow slowly on the long note and faster on the short one, so that you end up back where you started.

20. Blow The Man Down — *Sea Shanty*

30

What are those curvy lines?

1. This curve  can mean two different things.
2. When it's between different notes it's called a *slur*.
   Those notes share the same bow.
3. When the notes are the same it's called a *tie*.
   They are played together as one long note.

☆ 21. Write 'slur' or 'tie' under each curve.   *Puzzle*

Look carefully at the bowing symbols as you go. They make the tune easier to play!

What are slurs and ties for?

1. *Slurs* can keep an even number of bows in each bar and help the tune to flow smoothly.
2. Imagine chopping your bow in half. Use half for each note of a slur. A sticker in the middle might help if you find this tricky.
3. *Ties* let you write a note of any length, wherever you need it.
4. In book 2 we'll find more uses for *slurs*, and we'll *slur* more notes to a bow too.

31

22. A Major Scale With Slurs — *Exercise*

23. D Major Scale With Slurs — *Exercise*

24. G Major Scale With Slurs — *Exercise*

25. Coulter's Candy — *Song, Robert Coltart, 1800s*

26. Botany Bay — *Song*

Try to keep your fingers still on the string if you don't need to move them. You can also roll them onto the next string instead of lifting them up.

33

29. Chan Eil Mo Leannan Ann An Seo (My Sweetheart)   *Gaelic*

30. School Dinners (Frère Jacques)   *French Round Song*

31. I Know Something You Don't Know (Camptown Races)

I collected ☐ stars in chapter three!

Chapter Four

Where does my fourth finger go?

You can use your fourth finger instead of the open string above.
It will stretch out another marble space away from your third finger.

Fourth fingers aren't naturally as strong as the others so it takes
longer to get a good sound. Keep trying, you will manage it!

☆ 1. Fourth Finger Mini Tunes   *Exercises*

☆ 2. Three Craws   *Song*

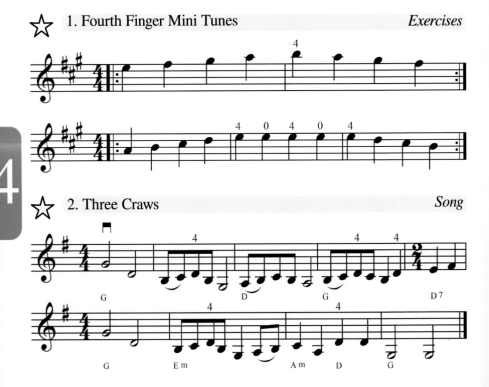

3. Ode to Joy (An Die Freude)
Ludwig van Beethoven, 1824

4. Oh The Britches Full Of Stitches
Irish Polka

Which notes are sharp?

If you look at the *key signature*, you can see it is made from ♯ *sharp* symbols. They are sitting on lines or spaces (like notes do) to tell you which notes are sharp.

☆ 5. Which notes are sharp? *Puzzle*
   Write the note names underneath each bar.

F, C

What are sharps anyway?

1. On the piano we usually play sharps with black notes to move them up by a *semitone* - the next tiny step.
2. A *whole tone* is made from two *semitones*.
3. On the violin E, A and D strings, *sharps* mean that the 2nd finger *stretches* a marble space away from the 1st.
4. Without a *sharp* they are *natural* so they sit close together instead.
5. We can use the arrows to help us remember! ⇩ ⇧

4

☆ 6. Stretched or close? *Puzzle*

   Draw an arrow above each note to show if your second finger would be stretched or close to first finger.

Where do my fingers go in C major?

1. In the key of C all the notes are *natural*.
2. We have no *sharps* so the marble spaces are in new places.
3. On the piano we would play *naturals* with the white notes, but on the violin we put our 2nd finger right next to our 1st.
4. This means that 3rd finger now has to stretch out!

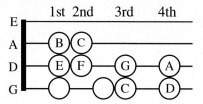

☆ 7. C Major Scale   *Exercise*

☆ 8. Tha Mi Sgìth (I Am Tired)   *Gaelic Song*

What is an arpeggio?

An *arpeggio* plays the most important notes of the *scale*.
In each of these arpeggios, stretch your second finger for the *major*,
then put it close to your first for the *minor*.
This raises or lowers it by a *semitone*.

9. A Major and Minor Arpeggios *Exercise*

10. D Major and Minor Arpeggios *Exercise*

11. G Major and Minor Arpeggios *Exercise*

7 Day Challenge!
Can you play every
day this week?

12. Do Your Ears Hang Low? *Singing Game*
   (Turkey In The Straw)

13. Morning Has Broken (Bunessan) *Song*

14. Wordsearch *Puzzle*

Scale
Dot
Major
Minor
Chord
Repeat
Rest
Down Bow
Up Bow
Slur
Sharp
Tie
Key
Count
Pluck
Beat

D	B	S	E	M	I	B	R	E	V	E	D
O	D	O	W	N	B	O	W	E	C	M	O
T	M	P	L	U	C	K	P	Q	S	A	S
T	I	U	P	B	O	W	I	Y	L	J	E
E	N	G	N	R	U	H	S	J	U	O	M
D	O	T	U	B	N	X	S	K	R	R	I
M	R	C	R	O	T	C	H	E	T	A	Q
I	F	T	E	S	W	C	A	Y	B	K	U
N	Q	R	P	C	H	O	R	D	E	D	A
I	V	E	E	A	F	H	P	G	A	A	V
M	Y	S	A	L	L	M	Z	E	T	I	E
D	O	T	T	E	D	Q	U	A	V	E	R

40

Where do my fingers go in G major?

Look out for the marble spaces
in new places!
In the key of G we have one *sharp*.
Can you see it in the chart?

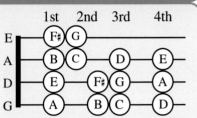

15 & 16. G Major Scale & Arpeggio, 2 Octaves   *Exercise*

17. London's Burning   *Round Song*

D 7   G   B m   E m   D   E m   D   G   D

G   D   G   B m   E m   D   G

18. Bonny Bobby Shafto (In And Out The Dusty Bluebells) *Song*

G   D   4

G   E m   A m   D   G

41

19. The Seven Step Polka — *Shetland Tune*

20. Ma, Ma, Will You Buy Me A Banana? — *March and Song*
(The Barren Rocks of Aden)

Don't practise until you get it right,
practise until you can't get it wrong!

21. The Bonnie Lass O Fyvie — *Song*

I collected ☐ stars in chapter four!

Chapter Five

What are intervals?

We give each note of the scale a number;

1   2   3   4   5   6   7   8

Then we call the distance between notes an *interval*.
1-2 is a 2nd, 1-3 is a 3rd, and so on...1-8 is called an octave (8ve).

☆   1. Let's work out the names of these intervals!   *Puzzle*
        Write the number in the box underneath each one.

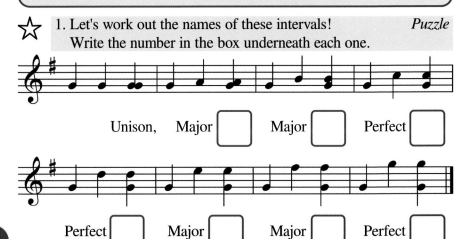

Unison,   Major ☐   Major ☐   Perfect ☐

Perfect ☐   Major ☐   Major ☐   Perfect ☐

5 What else are the note numbers for?

Arpeggios and *chords* are made from the odd numbers of the scale.
The chord symbols tell us which *scale* they are made from.
When you play the notes all at once you get a *chord*.
When the notes are played one at a time, that's an *arpeggio*.

43

How fast do we play?

1. We measure speed, or *tempo*, in *beats per minute* or B.P.M. for short. Your metronome lets you set the B.P.M.
2. When we play something new, we set it very slow and gradually speed up as we get to know the tune.
4. We write down the B.P.M. above the time signature.
5. This table shows different ways to describe tempo.
6. You can use the B. P. M., the Italian word, or both.

B.P.M.	Speed	Italian
40-60	Broad and slow	*Largo*
66-76	Slow	*Adagio*
76-108	Walking pace	*Andante*
108-120	Moderate speed	*Moderato*
120-156	Fast	*Allegro*
156-176	Faster	*Vivace*
168-200	Very Fast	*Presto*

☆ 6. The Wheels On The Bus   *Song*
   (Here We Go Round The Mulberry Bush)
   Use your metronome to work out which tempo best suits!

45

What are the numbers and lines for?

Here we have first and second time repeats.
The first time play number 1, the second time play 2 instead.

7. Ye Banks And Braes   *Robert Burns, 1791*

8. S' Iomadh Rud A Chunnaic Mi (Many Things Did I See) *Song*

9. Mairi's Wedding (Gaol Mo Chridhe-sa Màiri Bhàn) *Song*

10. Mrs MacLeod of Raasay *Reel, Sir Alex MacDonald, 1700s*

47

What are these tunes for?

Many of the tunes we have met so far are from songs;
others are for dancing.
Waltzes have three beats to a bar.
Marches and *reels* (so far) both have four beats to a bar,
but reels tend to go faster.
Polkas can go quite fast too - they can have two or four beats.

☆ 11. Dòmhnull Beag An t-Siùcair (Wee Donald Of The Sweets)

☆ 12. Thistle Of Scotland (Foghnan na h-Alba)   *March and Song*

5

48

Can we bow in other ways?

Slurs so far have been smooth.
We can break them into separate notes that still share the same bow, making it sound as if we've changed bow when we haven't.
We call this *broken slurs* or *hooked bowing*.

Symbol	Name	Meaning
//	Retake	Lift your bow in a circle, place it carefully ready for the next note.
⊓	Down Bow	Your bow moves downwards.
V	Up Bow	Your bow moves towards towards the sky.
‿	Slur	Notes smoothly share a bow.
	Staccato	Each note is played short, with space in between.
	Broken Slur	Notes share the bow with a gap between them.
	Straight Slur	A tidier way to draw a broken slur. We'll use these for Strathspeys in book 2.
⌒	Fermata	Pause

☆ 13. I Won't Marry You

Song

5

14. Donkey Riding (Highland Laddie) — *Regimental March*

15. The Rowan Tree — *Song, Carolina Oliphant, 1700s*

I collected ☐ stars in chapter five!

Chapter Six

Can we use other time signatures?

1. You'll remember from Chapter Three that the '4' at the bottom of a time signature tells us that we are counting *single beats*.
2. If it says '8' instead, we will be counting *half beats*.
3. *Simple time* is when the number on top is 2 or 4.
4. When we use this for multiples of 3 it is called *compound time*.

☆ 1. Counting Beats   *Puzzle*

a. How many half beats are there in each of these bars?
b. How many groups of 3 half beats can you count in each bar?

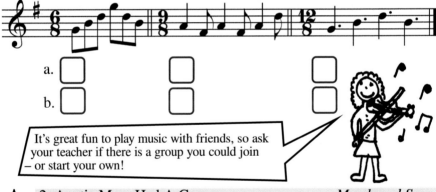

a. ☐   ☐   ☐

b. ☐   ☐   ☐

> It's great fun to play music with friends, so ask your teacher if there is a group you could join – or start your own!

☆ 2. Auntie Mary Had A Canary   *March and Song*

Why count groups of three?

When we play faster tunes, such as jigs, with these *compound* time signatures, we don't have time to count all the beats individually. We split them into groups of 3 half beats and count those instead.

 3. Time Signatures   *Puzzle*

   a. Write in the time signature for each of these bars.
   b. Write in the box how many beats (groups of 3 quavers) you would count if the tune was played quickly.

Remember to stop and check your bow hold. That makes everything easier.

4. Speed Bonnie Boat   *Song*

6

What are jigs?

Jigs are dance tunes that move in groups of three quavers.
In Scotland, we usually play jigs with a *swing* even when the groups of 3 are written evenly.

So, if it appears like this, it will sound like this.

5. The Butterfly

Irish Slip Jig

6. The Muckin O Geordie's Byre

Jig and Song

7. Rocking The Baby

Pipe Jig

Keep your fingers as still as possible, you can go faster that way!

6

What is syncopation?

1. We are already familiar with these rhythms...

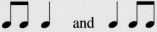 and

2. Now we can put the crotchet in between the quavers like this...

We could also write it as...

3. To help play it, we can say *te-ta-te* or *ba-na-na*.
4. It can feel a bit awkward at first but the broken slurs will help.

☆ 8. I Know A Song That'll Get On Your Nerves   *Song*

Sing the song to help you learn the tune, or say 'potato' in the syncopated notes!

☆ 9. Ten Green Bottles   *Song*

55

10. You Canny Shove Your Granny Off A Bus — *Song*

11. Oh Susanna! — *Song, Stephen Foster, 1848*

I collected ☐ stars in chapter six!

Christmas Tunes

1. Jingle Bells — *Song, James Lord Pierpont, 1800s*

2. Deck The Halls (Nos Galan) — *Welsh Carol, 1500s*

3. Christmas Lullaby (Tàladh Chrìosda) — *Gaelic Carol*

57

4. We Wish You A Merry Christmas
English Carol

5. Silent Night (Stille Nacht)
Franz Xaver Gruber, 1818

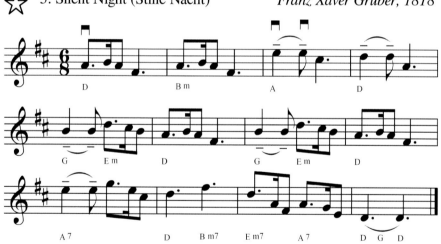

I collected ☐ Christmas stars!

Party Tunes

☆ Auld Lang Syne   *Song, Robert Burns, 1788*

☆ Happy Birthday   *Song, Patty and Mildred Hill, 1893*

I collected ☐ stars in this book!